Feeling...

Shy

First published in 1997 by Franklin Watts
96 Leonard Street, London EC2A 4RH

© Franklin Watts 1997

Franklin Watts Australia
14 Mars Road
Lane Cove
NSW 2006
Australia

Series editor: Helen Lanz
Series designer: Kirstie Billingham
Consultant: Anne Peake, Principal Psychologist

A CIP catalogue record for this book
is available from the British Library.

ISBN 0 7496 2599 6

10 9 8 7 6 5 4 3 2 1

Dewey Classification 152.4

Printed at Oriental Press, Dubai, U.A.E.

Feeling...

Shy

Sally Hewitt

Illustrated by Rhian Nest James

FRANKLIN WATTS

LONDON • NEW YORK • SYDNEY

Tomoko is 6 years old. She has just moved into a new flat
with her mum and dad. Mum is going to have a baby very soon.
Tomoko is shy when she meets new people.
When she feels shy, she doesn't want to talk or smile.

Do you feel shy sometimes?

Kenny is 6 years old too. He lives with his mum and dad, his older sister Bridget and his little brother Russ. Sometimes Kenny is too shy to answer questions or to show his work at school. He feels embarrassed and doesn't want to look silly in front of his friends.

What do you do when you feel shy?

Tomoko is getting ready to go to her new school.
She looks a bit worried. Mum knows that Tomoko is quiet
and finds it hard to make new friends. "Everyone feels
a bit shy on their first day in a new school," Mum says.
"But I don't know any of the other children at school," says Tomoko.
"I'm sure your teacher will help you to find a friend," says Mum.

6

Mum and Dad and Tomoko meet Kenny
and his mum at the school gate. Kenny's mum is very friendly.
She says, "Kenny is in your class, Tomoko. He'll look after you."
Kenny smiles at Tomoko. "Hello," he says.
Tomoko is too shy to say hello. She looks down and misses seeing Kenny's
friendly smile. She is worried that he might not like her.

Miss Travers introduces Tomoko to the class.

Everyone says "Hello Tomoko". Tomoko just looks at the floor.

"I think she's shy," says Kenny.

"What would you like to do, Tomoko?" asks Miss Travers.

"I'll help her use the computer," says Kenny.

"That's kind Kenny, but let Tomoko choose," says Miss Travers.

Tomoko spots some modelling clay.
She sits down and starts to make a model.
Kenny sits next to her. "I'm making an aeroplane,"
he says. "What are you making?"
Tomoko doesn't answer him.

Tomoko makes lots of beautiful little animals.
Kenny holds one up and calls out, "Look,
Tomoko has made a bear!"
Tomoko speaks for the first time.
She says, "It's not a bear, it's a panda!"

Everyone laughs, except Kenny.
He goes bright red. He wishes he
could hide.

10

Now Kenny feels shy because he is embarrassed.
He hates being wrong – he feels silly. Miss Travers quickly says,
"Pandas and bears look very alike, Kenny."
"We want to make a panda like Tomoko's," say Robert and Anjula.

Tomoko feels pleased that the children like her panda.
She shows them all how to make one. Kenny makes a panda, too,
and soon forgets to feel embarrassed.

11

At breaktime all the children run out into the playground.
Kenny is the first out because he wants to play football.
They forget about Tomoko. Miss Travers holds out her hand
and says, "Come with me Tomoko and we'll go outside together."

They watch some children playing a skipping game.
"Would you like to join in?" Miss Travers asks Tomoko.
Tomoko shakes her head. She feels too shy to join in
but she wishes she had a friend to play with.
Everyone is having fun, but she feels lonely and left out.

When they get back to the classroom, the children all make a card
and practise their best writing. Kenny makes a mistake
and rubs it with his finger. Now there is a horrid black smudge on his card.
He hides it in his lunchbox.

14

Miss Travers asks if any of the children
would like to show their cards to the class.
Tomoko is pleased with her card and shows it to Miss Travers.
"That's lovely, Tomoko," she says. "Hold it up for everyone to see."
Kenny keeps his card in his lunch box. He doesn't think it is very good
so he doesn't want anyone to see it!

After lunch, Luke cuts his knee in the playground.
Miss Travers has to take him inside and leave Tomoko by herself.

Tomoko watches Kenny and his friends playing football.
She wants to join in, but she doesn't try to
in case someone says, "Go away, we don't want you!"

16

Kenny sees Tomoko standing by herself.
He remembers he should be looking after her.
"Let's ask Tomoko to join in," he says.
Justin says "No! I don't like her.
She always looks cross and grumpy."

17

Miss Travers has come outside again.

She says, "Tomoko isn't really cross. She's just shy.

I expect she's worried that you won't like her."

"I like her," says Kenny and gives Tomoko a big smile.

Tomoko sees Kenny smiling at her and feels pleased.

She smiles for the first time that day.

18

"You look nice when you smile, Tomoko," says Justin.

Miss Travers looks at her watch. "Playtime is over," she says.

"Let's ask Tomoko to play with us tomorrow!" says Kenny.

"OK," says Justin.

Tomoko thinks smiling is a good way
to start making friends when you feel shy.

After school, Tomoko gives her mum a big hug.
Kenny's mum smiles at Tomoko.
"Would you like to come to tea, Tomoko?" she asks.
Kenny's big sister Bridget and her friend come running up.
Tomoko looks at them and shakes her head.

Bridget doesn't know Tomoko is shy.
She thinks Tomoko is being rude. Mum knows
it's difficult to do too many new things in one day!
"Would Kenny like to come to tea with us first?" she asks.
Kenny nods. Tomoko is pleased. She likes Kenny because
he has been really friendly and helpful.

Kenny's mum is holding baby Russ in her arms.

Tomoko thinks about her new baby and wants to make friends.

She smiles at Russ but he doesn't smile back.

He hides his face in Mum's jumper!

22

Tomoko tries to make him smile.
She makes Russ's toy dog Woof say "Hello Russ"
in a funny voice. Russ is shy of Tomoko,
but he isn't shy of Woof. He starts to giggle.
Mum laughs. "Now you've made two new friends, Tomoko!" she says.

Tomoko gives her mum the card she made at school.

"It's beautiful," she says and shows it to everyone.

"You are clever Tomoko," says Bridget.

"Where's your card Kenny?"

He frowns and puts his hands in his pockets.

He is still worried about the smudge.

24

Bridget and Carol walk on ahead and Mum gives Kenny a hug.
"Did you make a card, too, Kenny?" she asks very quietly.
She realises that he might be embarrassed about his card
and wonders if he is worried that Bridget might tease him.

"My card is no good!" says Kenny.
"You like Tomoko's much better than mine!"
"But I haven't seen yours yet," says Mum.
Kenny brings his card out of his lunch box
and gives it to her. "It's got a smudge!" he says.

"What a shame," says Mum. "But I don't mind the smudge.
I'll put it by my bed because you made it specially for me."
Kenny is happy because Mum likes the card.
No one else will notice the smudge if she puts it by her bed.

When Dad comes in Kenny says, "A new girl
called Tomoko came to school today.
She was so shy she wouldn't talk or smile,
but I looked after her and made her smile."
Dad says, "Well done Kenny. It's kind to help people
when they're feeling shy and left out."

"You were shy today too, Kenny," says Mum.
"You felt too shy to give me my card."
"Kenny thought I wouldn't like his card.
But I like it so much I've put it by my bed," says Mum.

"So, Kenny, you helped Tomoko to stop feeling shy,
and Mum helped you to stop feeling shy," laughs Dad.
What helps you to stop feeling shy?

Notes for teachers and parents

Young children often feel shy when they meet new people or have to cope with an unfamiliar situation. They worry that no one will like them or that they will make a mistake and look silly. Feeling shy can often make children appear to be unfriendly or rude, and that can make matters worse.

A sympathetic adult can help children to build confidence and to learn how to cope in situations that make them feel shy. Through trying to understand emotions, strategies can be learned about how to deal with them.

In the story, Tomoko and Kenny are confronted with situations that make them shy or embarrassed.

These incidents can be used as starting points to discuss what can make children feel that way: they may recognise some of their own feelings and behaviour in the story, or it may help them to understand why someone has reacted to them in a certain way.

The adults in the story provide helpful support for the children. They are used as a way to highlight why children behave as they do when they feel shy, providing an insight that children themselves might not be aware of.

The following questions about some of the incidents in the story could be used to generate discussion.

30

Further discussion and activities

• On page 6, Tomoko is feeling shy because she doesn't know any of the other children at her new school. Do you feel shy when you meet new people?

• What is Tomoko worried about on page 7? What does she do which shows that she is worried? What do you do when you feel shy or worried?

• What happens to make Kenny go bright red on page 10? What does Kenny wish he could do? What makes you embarrassed?

• On page 11, who makes Kenny forget to feel embarrassed? How does she do that?

• On page 17, Justin says he doesn't like Tomoko. Why doesn't he like her?
Do you think he is right or wrong about Tomoko?

• How does Kenny make Tomoko smile on page 18? What could you do to help someone to stop feeling shy?

• On pages 28 and 29, Mum, Dad and Kenny talk about feeling shy. Everyone feels shy sometimes. It helps to talk to someone you trust about how you feel.

It might be helpful to follow up the discussion or story with some activities. Some suggested activities are listed below.

• Make a list of ideas in the story that can help you stop feeling shy. Which is your favourite idea? You could try it the next time you feel shy.

• When people feel shy, they sometimes go bright red or try to hide their feelings. Draw a picture of someone feeling shy.

• Tomoko has gone to tea at Kenny's house. She is feeling very shy of Kenny's sister Bridget so she hides behind a chair.

Draw a picture or write a story about what happens next to stop Tomoko feeling shy of Bridget.

31

Useful words

embarrassed — A feeling you can get if everyone notices you when you don't want them to, or if you or someone else does something which makes you feel silly.

to be friendly — Someone is friendly to you when they smile and ask if they can help you when you are feeling lonely.

grumpy — A feeling you can get when you are cross or unhappy. It makes you frown and look unfriendly and sometimes you may even say horrid things.

to feel left out — You can feel left out when nobody notices you and nobody asks you to join in the fun even though you would like to join in.

lonely — You can feel lonely when everyone else has a friend, but you have no one to play with.

mistake — You make a mistake when you get something wrong without meaning to. Everyone makes mistakes sometimes, even parents and teachers. You can usually put a mistake right or try again.

rude — If you smile at someone and say "hello" but they frown at you and won't smile back, they seem to be very rude. Really, they might only be feeling shy.

shy — A feeling you get when you are worried about meeting new people and going to new places. You may not feel like smiling or talking to anyone.

to tease someone — Teasing is when someone plays a trick on you or pretends to be unkind, but they don't really mean it. For example, they might say "All my friends can come to my party except you!" and then say, "Not really, I was only teasing!" Being teased can make you feel unhappy.

to feel silly — You can feel silly when you have made a mistake and everyone laughs.

32